A Tiny **Baby Brother**

Tiffany Robinson
Feb 17, 2022

Written by Tiffany Robinson
Illustrated by Yoko Matsuoka

Also by Tiffany Robinson

Zoe's Sidewalk
Zoe's Garden

Praise for "Zoe's Sidewalk"

Enjoyed reading this sweet story with my 6-year-old daughter. Love the confidence Zoe gained when she realized she could make a difference and change her neighborhood for the better... I highly recommend.

Kendra H.
Amazon review

For Raymond

"A baby is coming
in just three months," Mama says.
I'll have a brother.

I listen, but I don't hear
him crying.
Daddy smiles. "Not yet!"
Mama takes my hand and places
it on her belly.
"Oh, oh!" He's moving.

"A baby is coming in just two months," Daddy says.

I'll have a brother.

I'll help make his bed.

I'll help put away his toys.

His room is next to mine.

Daddy buys a crib and hangs a big "J" on the wall.
Mama rubs my hair.
"A baby is coming
in just one more month," they say.
Baby Jackson.

They go to the doctor.

But Mama doesn't come home.

Cousin Tina keeps me.

"Mama had the baby today,"

Daddy says when he gets home.

"We'll visit in the morning."

My brother is here.

He's with Mama.

Daddy says he's very tiny and cannot come home yet.

Daddy wakes me in the morning
and we go to the hospital.
Mama meets us there.
We wash our hands in a big sink.
Babies like clean hands.

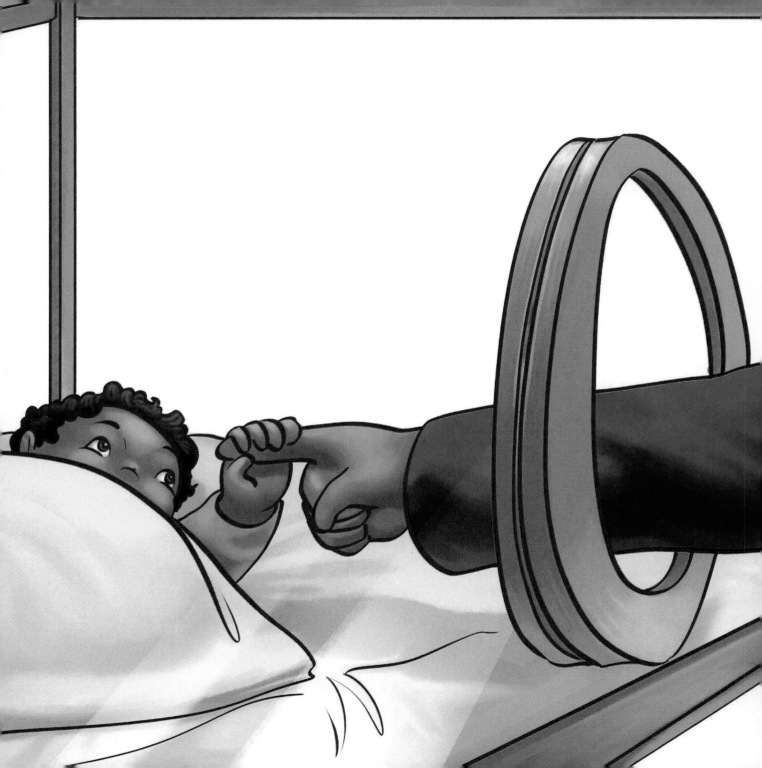

I see Jackson.

He's in a tiny crib, but I can hold his hand.

Daddy picks him up, and I sit on Mama's lap.

We hold Jackson.

"When will he come home?"

Mama says, "Soon, when he is bigger."

I have a brother.

He sleeps at the hospital.

We go every day.

Mama and Daddy teach me to
hold Jackson.

I read books to him.

I hold him, and he looks at me.

He loves me.

And I love him too.

Today, Jackson's car seat is next to me as we drive.

He is coming home!

I sit close to him.

He lies on the couch and looks at me while I look at him.

This is my brother.

He was a tiny baby, but now he is home.

Made in the USA
Monee, IL
12 November 2021

Beavers

Quinn M. Arnold

CREATIVE EDUCATION
CREATIVE PAPERBACKS

seedlings

Published by Creative Education and Creative Paperbacks
P.O. Box 227, Mankato, Minnesota 56002
Creative Education and Creative Paperbacks
are imprints of The Creative Company
www.thecreativecompany.us

Design by Ellen Huber; production by Joe Kahnke
Art direction by Rita Marshall
Printed in China

Photographs by Alamy (Arco Images GmbH, mauritius images
GmbH), Creative Commons Wikimedia (Sylvain Haye), Dreamstime
(Asakalaskas, Chase Dekker, Jnjhuz), Getty Images (Sven Zacek),
iStockphoto (LucyF, NeilLockhart), Minden Pictures (Ingo Arndt,
Dietmar Nill), National Geographic Creative (JOEL SARTORE,
NATIONAL GEOGRAPHIC PHOTO ARK; KONRAD WOTHE/
MINDEN PICTURES), Newscom (Bernd Zoller imageBROKER),
PublicDomainPictures (Lilla Frerichs), Shutterstock (Agustin
Esmoris, Bill Frische, Christian Musat), SuperStock (Ken Baehr/
Alaska Stock - Design Pics)

Library of Congress Cataloging-in-Publication Data
Names: Arnold, Quinn M., author.
Title: Beavers / Quinn M. Arnold.
Series: Seedlings.
Includes bibliographical references and index.
Summary: A kindergarten-level introduction to beavers,
covering their growth process, behaviors, the dams they call
home, and such defining features as their flat tails.
Identifiers: LCCN 2016054373 / ISBN 978-1-60818-865-9
(hardcover) / ISBN 978-1-62832-480-8 (pbk) / ISBN 978-1-
56660-913-5 (eBook)

Subjects: LCSH: Beavers—Juvenile literature.
Classification: LCC QL737.R632 A76 2017 / DDC 599.37—dc23

CCSS: RI.K.1, 2, 3, 4, 5, 6, 7;
RI.1.1, 2, 3, 4, 5, 6, 7; RF.K.1, 3; RF.1.1

First Edition HC 9 8 7 6 5 4 3 2 1
First Edition PBK 9 8 7 6 5 4 3 2 1